Merrily Harpur was educated at Headington School, Oxford, and Trinity College, Dublin. She is a freelance cartoonist and writer whose drawings have appeared in numerous magazines, books and newspapers, most frequently in the *Guardian*. She has published a collection of her strip cartoons from *Punch*, *The Nightmares of Dream Topping*, and also written for the *Guardian*, *The Times*, the *Sunday Times* and *Departures* magazine. She is currently writing a historical novel.

She lives both in England and in Ireland, where she fly-fishes and is building up a priceless collection of waterproof clothing, which she hopes eventually to leave to a cats' home.

Unheard of Ambridge

Merrily Harpur

PENGUIN BOOKS

Published by the Penguin Group
27 Wrights Lane, London W8 5TZ, England
Viking Penguin Inc., 40 West 23rd Street, New York, New York 10010, USA
Penguin Books Australia Ltd, Ringwood, Victoria, Australia
Penguin Books Canada Ltd, 2801 John Street, Markham, Ontario, Canada L3R 1B4
Penguin Books (NZ) Ltd, 182–190 Wairau Road, Auckland 10, New Zealand

Penguin Books Ltd, Registered Offices: Harmondsworth, Middlesex, England

Most of these cartoons were first published in the *Listener* between April 1988 and April 1989
This collection first published by Penguin Books 1989

3 5 7 9 10 8 6 4 2

Printed in Great Britain by
Richard Clay Ltd, Bungay, Suffolk

INTRODUCTION
By Jean-Paul of Grey Gables.

Allo Mesdames et Messieurs!
'Ow right you are to be dipping into zis littel book, testing ze flaveur!

No vrai bon viveur such as oneself, would ever gobble down an 'ot pot of such rich and subtle pleasures ....

And now a confession. Ah 'ave been moi-même a resident of Un'eard of Ambridge. Oui!
Ah 'ave produced mon greatest dishes zere:
Black pudding gâteau à la Snatch Foster;
fresh from John Higgs' greenhouse, chrysanthemum hearts in thrips; ....
....John Dory lips glazed with Carnal Fire by Revlon, rushed straight to the table from the make-up bag of Prue Forrest; etc. etc.
Zose were ze days.

John Higgs.
Mr. Woolley's
Gardener.

SHANE, OF NELSON'S
WINE BAR, IS AT
ALL TIMES SELF-
EXPLANATORY.

OF THE 365 WINDOWS IN MONSTROUS, RAMBLING BRIDGE FARM THERE IS ONE NO-ONE CAN ACCOUNT FOR .....

IF YOU MENTION IT TO ANY OF THE LOCALS YOU ARE MET BY A WALL OF SILENCE — THE SHUTTERS COMING DOWN OVER THE SULLEN PEASANT FACES.

PEGGY

SID

WALTER

JACK

YOU COULD TORTURE MARTHA WOODFORD.... BUT SHE **WOULDN'T BLAB**.

©Merily Harper 1988.

©!!

HISSS

TELL ME OR I VILL JEMBLE EP YOUR TILL RECEIPTS!

ONLY MRS. POTTER SEEMS TO KNOW THE WAY IN...

FROSTED GLASS

GRAHAM LOOKS AFTER
THE COWS AT BROOKFIELD
& IS A COUNTRY 'N WESTERN
AFFICIONADO.
SOMETIMES HE HITS TOWN.

SQUELCH

SQUELCH

A DAY IN THE LIFE OF HERR RODWAY:

Winceyette mask

ZZZ... MUMBLE ....ZE BOOM....ZE BOOM....
MIEN GOTT.... HES IT PEAKED YET?...

© Merily Harpur 1988.

HE TOSSES &
TURNS ALL
NIGHT IN
HIS QUEEN
ANNE RECTORY
BEFORE
GOING DOWN
TO A
TYPICAL
SHARK'S
BREAKFAST

Two hedgehogs Walker!
Just the spines!

IMMEDIATELY
HERR
RODWAY

Asbestos
mask

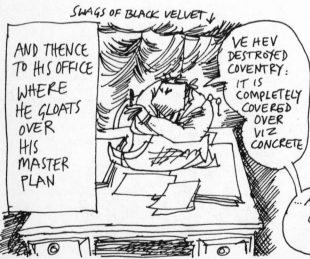

SWAGS OF BLACK VELVET

AND THENCE
TO HIS OFFICE
WHERE
HE GLOATS
OVER
HIS
MASTER
PLAN

VE HEV
DESTROYED
COVENTRY:
IT IS
COMPLETELY
COVERED
OVER
VIZ
CONCRETE

Here is ze
Wienetorte
complètement
covered wi3
cream which
you ordered
m. Rodway.
And now, eef
you will excuse
me I must go
out and blow
my nose

...AND NEXT—AMBRIDGE! Ve vill
cover it viz precincts, underpasses,
VALKVAYS, concrete litter bins
und terrace restaurants!

Extremism goes
straight to my
sinuses, Prue

THE BISHOP OF
FELPERSHAM
BELIEVES CHRISTIANS
CAN STILL MAKE
A POSITIVE
CONTRIBUTION
IN TODAY'S
CHANGING
SOCIETY OF
DISCO-GOERS
AND AIDS
SUFFERERS

DRY ROT AS A METAPHOR

LORD NETHERBOURNE
CHAIR OF FELPERSHAM
W.R.P. IS CAROLINE
BONE'S UNCLE AND
THE MOST UPPER
CLASS PERSON MR.
WOOLLEY KNOWS OF.

IT'S IMPOSSIBLE TO GET WORKERS TO STAND SHOULDER TO SHOULDER THESE DAYS, EXCEPT AT A COCKTAIL PARTY.

.... THERE IS A LEGEND THAT ALBINO HORROBINS
    INFEST THE SEWERS OF AMBRIDGE.....

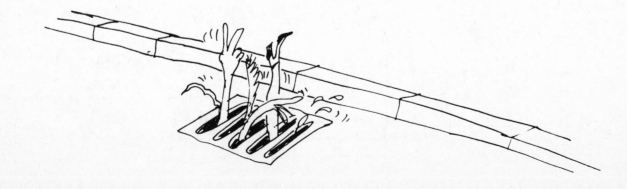

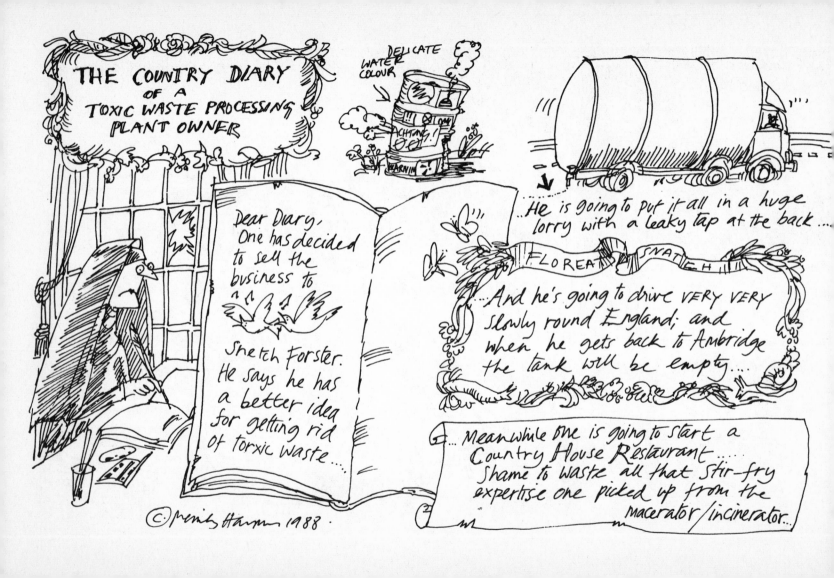

SULTRY PRUE FORREST,
DOYENNE OF JAMS &
CHUTNEYS, IS THINKING
OF BEATING HER
PRESERVING PANS
INTO EARRINGS.

THE CORN IS AS
HIGH AS AN ELEPHANT'S
EYE, ACCORDING TO
THE AGRICULTURAL STORY
EDITOR.

CAPTAIN
GODFREY WENDOVER
IS PEGGY ARCHER'S
SEAFARING PARAMOUR,
FROM AUSTRALIA.

horn pipe

songline →

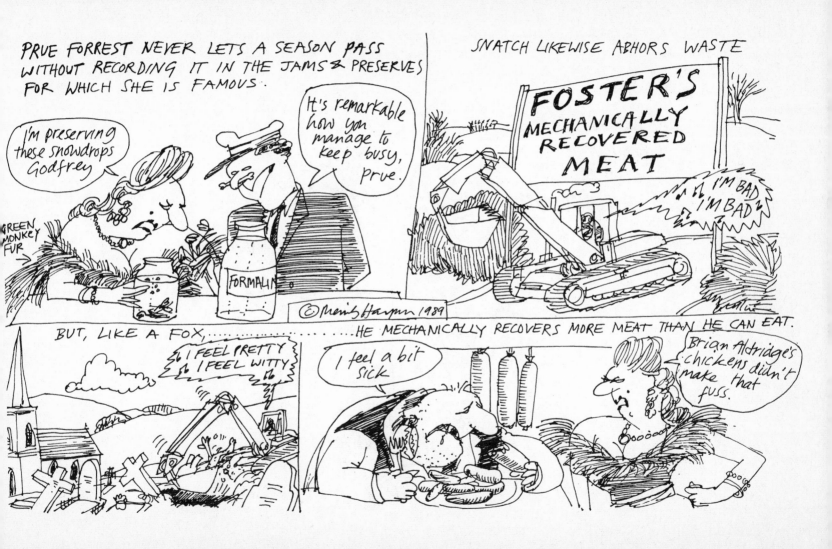

THERE IS A
HORROBIN
SOMEWHERE
IN THIS BIRD BOX.

CAN YOU
SPOT IT?

THE CHRYSANTHEMUM SEASON IS ON THE WANE, THE GLADIOLI SEASON NOT YET UNDER WAY; **JOHN HIGGS** IS IN THE GREEN-HOUSE AT **GREY GABLES** WRITING THE COUNTRY DIARY COLUMN FOR THE GUARDIAN.

JOHN INNES NO. 786

© Merrily Harpur 1989

"How the damp days of this unseasonably mild winter retain the fragrances of heath & woodland! As I write there is the pungent tang of wood smoke from the barn conversions where antipodean Godfrey Wendover plies the ancient trade of charcoal burning..."..

YE OLDE WISHING BARBIE

"The other day I was leaning on a gate when the familiar scent of reconstituted meat slurry heralded my friend Snatch Foster, born & bred in a totally unconverted cottage. As we watched the unseasonably numerous magpies he wryly quoted the old saying"....

One for sorrow....

....Two for a good larf;
Three for you wish you 'adn't;
Four for a knuckle sandwich;
Foive for protection;
Six for gold
Seven for not another squeak out of you, me ol' pal me ol' beauty.

SNATCH FOSTER!
THE WORLD'S MOST
FEARED
KISSAGRAM.

IN AMONGST THE PRESERVING PANS, PRUE FORREST IS WRITING HER COLUMN FOR THE BORSETSHIRE ECHO ENTITLED 'BERT FRY DOESN'T KNOW THE HALF OF IT.' THIS WEEK THE SPOTLIGHT FALLS ON BAGGY....

"...FOR INNUMERABLE GENERATIONS BAGGY'S FAMILY HAVE BEEN FRIGHTENING AWAY ROOKS & PIGEONS IN THE OLD TRADITIONAL MANNER, BY MEANS OF A DISMISSIVE GESTURE & POLITE COUGH. BUT NOW"......

Gorn out of that ye little varmints, ye devils!

ICI

Killing isn't he?

"...A NEW BREED OF SCARER ROAMS THE COUNTRYSIDE, HONKING BMW HORNS, HOOTING WITH LAUGHTER, & CLANKING EMPTY LAGER CANS."...

EEEK!

CROAK

RODWAYS

PURVEYOR OF SCARE-CROWS TO THE N.T. "your worst nightmare is our command." MODEL NO. 3759# "TIM BEAUCHAMP"

AAARS

..."WHILE POOR BAGGY IS REDUCED TO SCARING OFF TOURISTS WHO STOP OFF ON THEIR WAY UP THE M6 TO ENJOY A PINT OF PIMMS IN THE GARDEN OF THE BULL. HE WANDERS UP TO THEM"...

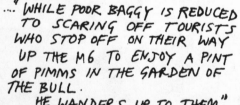

ICI

...."AND SUDDENLY BLOWS HIS NOSE ON A BENT BEER MAT HE KEEPS FOR THE PURPOSE"....

-EEEK! AAARS

-CROAK.

© Merrily Harpur 1989

BAGGY, SUCKING
HIS THUMB & FONDLING
HIS SECURITY
FERTILISER BAG.